Contents

AGES 10–11
LITERACY

Test 1 Unstressed vowels

Some **vowels** in longer words are **not stressed** and are difficult to hear.

envelope

Fill in the missing vowels.

1. di____mond

2. accident____l

3. entr____nce

4. diff____rent

5. deod____rant

6. myst____ry

7. cru____l

8. int____resting

9. eff____rt

10. monast____ry

11. lunch____on

12. sep____rate

13. butt____n

14. skel____ton

15. ph____tographer

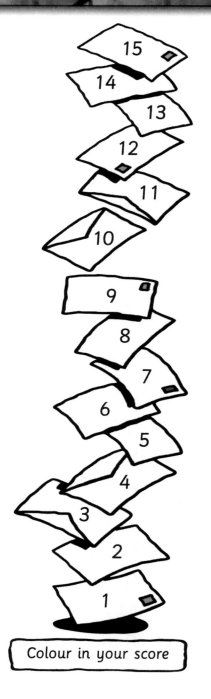

Colour in your score

Test 1

Test 2 Root words

A **root word** is a word to which **prefixes** or **suffixes** may be added. Sometimes the root word is **easy** to see. Sometimes the root word is **harder** to work out.

bicycle (root word = cycle)   beautiful (root word = beauty)

Work out the root word for each of these words.

1.   befriend _____

2.   assistance _____

3.   centimetre _____

4.   disability _____

5.   beggar _____

6.   engineer _____

7.   exchange _____

8.   kingdom _____

9.   brightness _____

10. imperfect _____

11. prefix _____

12. service _____

13. superman _____

14. duckling _____

15. withhold _____

Colour in your score

Test 2

Test 3 Dashes

A **dash** holds words apart. It is stronger than a comma but is not as strong as a full stop.

I have got a new bike – a mountain bike.

Decide where to put the dash in each sentence.

1. I had my favourite meal spaghetti.

2. I love apples Ben hates them!

3. One boy looked strange he was wearing a mask.

4. I won a prize for coming first in spelling.

5. My uncle appeared laughing as usual.

6. Christopher Wren built a famous cathedral St Paul's.

7. Mr Smith has a sports car a silver one.

8. I love music especially pop music.

9. On the sand I found something interesting an old chest.

10. Work hard or you will never get a good job!

11. I know someone very brave my friend Sarah.

12. Tom collects insects especially beetles.

13. Mount Pico is in the Azores a group of islands.

14. I saw a good programme last night a monster film.

15. My room overlooks a wood a small dark wood.

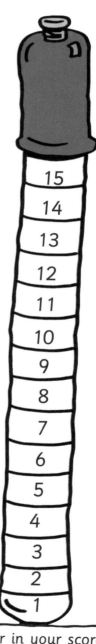

15
14
13
12
11
10
9
8
7
6
5
4
3
2
1

Colour in your score

Test 4 Parts of speech

Words may be divided into groups called **parts of speech**. Three important parts of speech are **nouns**, **verbs** and **adjectives**.

This is a **noun**. It is a **naming** word.

The sad baby was crying.

This is an **adjective**. It is a **describing** word. It tells us more about the **noun**.

This is a **verb**. It is a word that describes **actions**.

Underline the noun in each sentence.

1. The red door was shut.

2. The poor old man had to sit down.

3. The wind howled and howled.

4. Some silly children were giggling.

5. My new car was metallic silver.

Underline the verb in each sentence.

6. On Mondays I always ride my bike.

7. Yesterday I ate fifteen biscuits!

8. Next week I will try much harder.

9. Mrs Baker cooked a lovely casserole.

10. Cross the road carefully.

Underline the adjective in each sentence.

11. The floor was slippery.

12. The rough sea crashed against the cliffs.

13. Some colourful birds landed in the garden.

14. In the forest it is scary.

15. My favourite uncle came to see me.

Colour in your score

Test 4

Test 5 Connectives

We sometimes join two **clause**s together by using a **connective**.

I like the summer   because   I go on holiday then.

clause 1   connective   clause 2

Choose the best connective to join each pair of clauses.

1. He was not tired _____ he had to go to bed. (nevertheless/and)

2. I couldn't decide whether to go _____ stay. (and/or)

3. She put up her umbrella _____ it was raining. (so that/because)

4. We stopped for a cup of tea _____ we were early. (as/so)

5. I ate my lunch _____ I went out. (because/before)

6. The cat chased the birds _____ they landed. (since/when)

7. I turned up the radio _____ I could hear it. (as/so that)

8. I won't go out _____ it is raining. (and/if)

9. If you are late _____ you will get into trouble. (when/then)

10. I had a wash _____ I went to the party. (in case/until)

11. I shouted _____ someone heard me. (until/because)

12. I could not do it _____ hard I tried. (however/in case)

13. I don't like cheese _____ my mum does. (and/but)

14. We went home _____ the match finished. (as soon as/until)

15. We ran fast _____ we were late. (after/because)

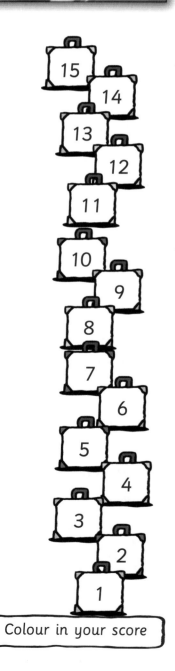

Colour in your score

Test 5

Test 6 Prefixes and suffixes

We add **prefixes** and **suffixes** to words to **change their meanings**.

accurate – **in**accurate

A **prefix** is added to the **beginning** of a word. It does **not** change the spelling of the root word.

happy – happi**ness**

A **suffix** is added to the **end** of a word. It may **sometimes** change the spelling of the root word.

Choose the correct prefix to complete each word.

1. _____graph (ex/auto)

2. _____legal (im/il)

3. _____port (de/mal)

4. _____patient (in/im)

5. _____approve (for/dis)

6. _____behave (dis/mis)

7. _____bark (em/en)

8. _____arrange (pre/pro)

Add the suffix to each root word.
Write the word you make.

9. confide (ence)   _____

10. bake (ery)   _____

11. communicate (ion)   _____

12. study (ent)   _____

13. replace (ment)   _____

14. serve (ice)   _____

15. friendly (ness)   _____

Colour in your score

Test 6

Test 7 Active and passive verbs

The footballer kicked the ball.

A verb is **active** when the subject of the sentence does the action.

The ball was kicked by the footballer.

A verb is **passive** when the subject of the sentence has the action done to it.

Decide if the verb in each sentence is active or passive.

1. The child wrote a story. _____

2. The books were written by the author. _____

3. The man rode his mountain bike. _____

4. The telephone was answered by the lady. _____

5. The shoes were worn by Sarah. _____

6. The squirrel climbed the tree. _____

7. The lion chased the antelope. _____

8. The cakes were eaten by Mrs Sallis. _____

9. I received a present yesterday. _____

10. The sword was waved by the pirate. _____

11. The farmer collected the eggs. _____

12. The snake slid along the ground. _____

13. The nest was made by the bird. _____

14. The song was sung by the pop singer. _____

15. I telephoned my friend. _____

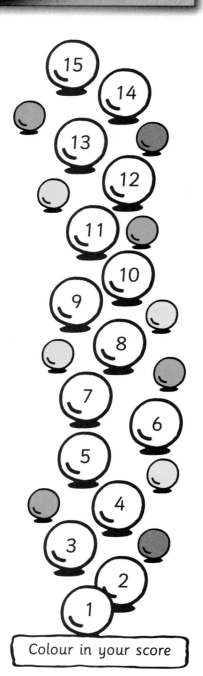

Colour in your score

Test 7

Test 8 Where do our words come from?

English is not just **one language**. It is made up of words taken from many **other languages**.

pizza (Italian)   yacht (Dutch)   vase (French)

Find the words we have borrowed from other languages.

ballerina	skipper	buffet	piano	cabaret
bracket	spaghetti	sketch	schooner	bouquet
opera	confetti	smuggle	landscape	duvet

The words from Italy all end in a vowel other than **e**.

1. _____   2. _____   3. _____

4. _____   5. _____

The words from France all end in **et**.

6. _____   7. _____   8. _____

9. _____   10. _____

The other words are all Dutch words.

11. _____   12. _____   13. _____

14. _____   15. _____

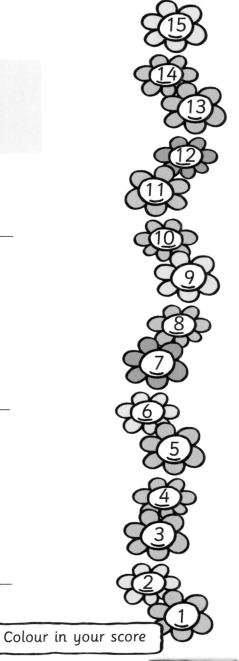

15
14
13
12
11
10
9
8
7
6
5
4
3
2
1

Colour in your score

Test 8

Test 9 Mnemonics

A **mnemonic** is a way of remembering the spelling of tricky words.

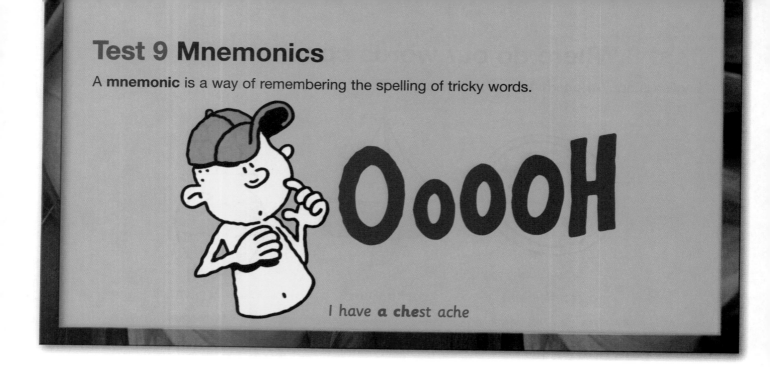

I have **a che**st ache

ambitious   believe   business   breadth

cereal   chocolate   conscience   government

island   knowledge   mathematics

piece   separate   soldier   whole

Find the word with the following word 'hiding' in it.

1. know _____

2. lie _____

3. them _____

4. pie _____

5. bit _____

6. late _____

7. bus _____

8. men _____

9. rat _____

10. bread _____

11. science _____

12. who _____

13. is _____

14. real _____

15. die _____

Colour in your score

Test 9

Test 10 Punctuation

Punctuation marks help us **make sense** of what we read. Where we put punctuation marks can make a difference!

I wore a hat. On my head
I wore some boots.

I wore a hat on my head.
I wore some boots.

Fill in the missing punctuation marks.

1. Dr Turner___s car was green.

2. Mrs Brown, who was getting angry___ shouted loudly.

3. "Don___t cross the busy road," Mrs Smith warned Tom.

4. Do you like oranges or lemons best___

5. During the night___ it rained heavily.

6. "Where's my dinner?___ the giant roared.

7. "I hate sprouts___" Sam shouted.

8. My brother hates music___ but I love it.

9. In my pocket I had a coin, a sweet___ a tissue and a badge.

10. The teachers___ room is next to the office.

11. Where are you going___

12. I___m nearly eleven.

13. The film doesn___t begin for an hour.

14. "Hands up___" the robber shouted.

15. ___My job can be dangerous," the police officer said.

Colour in your score

Test 10

Test 11 **Word origins**

The English language has been influenced by **many other languages**. Understanding the **origins** of words sometimes helps us to spell them.

The word **phone** comes from a Greek word meaning **sound**.

*micro***phone**   *tele***phone**

spectator	liberty	signal	liberal	spectacles
audience	liberate	audible	script	signature
describe	scribble	spectacular	auditorium	design

Write some English words we get from these Latin words.

signum (meaning a sign)

1. _____   2. _____   3. _____

liber (meaning free)

4. _____   5. _____   6. _____

audio (meaning I hear)

7. _____   8. _____   9. _____

scribo (meaning I write)

10. _____   11. _____   12. _____

specto (meaning I watch)

13. _____   14. _____   15. _____

15 14 13 12 11 10 9 8 7 6 5 4 3 2 1

Colour in your score

Test 11

Test 12 Complex sentences

A **clause** is a **group of words** which can be used as a **whole sentence** or as **part of a sentence**. Many sentences contain **more than one** clause.

This sentence contains two clauses.

The stars twinkled   *and*   *the moon shone.*

clause 1   clause 2

Write and say how many clauses there are in each sentence. (1 or 2)

1. I like West Highland Terrier dogs. _____

2. Some cats stay out all night. _____

3. I fell over while we were playing. _____

4. The cat chased the birds that landed on the grass. _____

5. I posted the letter in the post box. _____

6. I bought the comic from the shop. _____

7. When the wind blew the trees swayed. _____

8. Last night I had stomach ache after I ate my tea. _____

9. Cows moo but don't bark. _____

10. Nelson's Column stands in the middle of London. _____

11. The man got stuck when the lift doors closed. _____

12. I went to Spain and visited Madrid. _____

13. My budgie escaped when I left its cage open. _____

14. The lady paid for her hat and left the shop. _____

15. The ugly troll waited patiently under the bridge. _____

Colour in your score

Test 12

Test 13 Proverbs

A **proverb** is a **wise saying** that has been around for a **long time**.

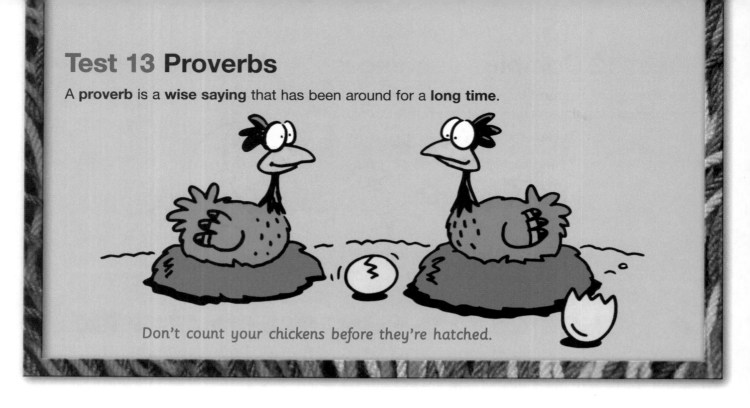

Don't count your chickens before they're hatched.

Match up the beginning and ending of each proverb.

1.	Absence makes the heart	than words.
2.	Beggars can't be	twice shy.
3.	Actions speak louder	never.
4.	Birds of a feather	less speed.
5.	Once bitten,	choosers.
6.	Every cloud has	out of mind.
7.	Too many cooks	you leap.
8.	Don't put all your eggs	grow fonder.
9.	More haste,	than one.
10.	Make hay while	flock together.
11.	Two heads are better	a silver lining.
12.	Better late than	in one basket.
13.	Look before	the sun shines.
14.	Out of sight,	saves nine.
15.	A stitch in time	spoil the broth.

Colour in your score

Test 14 Syllables

Words can be broken down into smaller parts, called **syllables**.

um / brel / la   (3 syllables)

Think of a suitable second syllable for each word. Write the words you make.

1.   de + ____ + mine =   _____

2.   u + ____ + form =   _____

3.   hos + ____ + al =   _____

4.   ex + ____ + lent =   _____

5.   at + ____ + tion =   _____

6.   dif + ____ + ent =   _____

7.   ad + ____ + ture =   _____

8.   syl + ____ + le =   _____

9.   par + ____ + chute =   _____

10.   in + ____ + duce =   _____

11.   be + ____ + ning =   _____

12.   e + ____ + tric =   _____

13.   Sep + ____ + ber =   _____

14.   pun + ____ + ment =   _____

15.   fa + ____ + ite =   _____

Colour in your score

Test 14

Test 15 Using dictionaries

You can use a **dictionary** to check the **spelling** of words.

hippapotamis   hippopotomus   hippopotamus

Each of the following words is spelt incorrectly.
Write each word correctly. Use a dictionary if necessary.

1.   ocasion   _____

2.   priviledge   _____

3.   fasinate   _____

4.   exitement   _____

5.   immidiate   _____

6.   reconise   _____

7.   mathmatics   _____

8.   dissappear   _____

9.   controll   _____

10. marrage   _____

11. rubarb   _____

12. temporey   _____

13. disasterous   _____

14. sissors   _____

15. enviroment   _____

Colour in your score

Test 15

Test 16 Spelling rules

Some **spelling rules** are helpful to remember. One common rule is: **i** (when it makes the sound **ee**) before **e** except after **c**.

I rec**ei**ved a p**ie**ce of cake.

Follow the rule. Choose ie or ei to complete each word.

1. bel_____ve

2. rec_____ve

3. c_____ling

4. ch_____f

5. p_____ce

6. rel_____f

7. f_____ld

8. perc_____ve

9. dec_____ve

10. dec_____t

11. lad_____s

12. pr_____st

13. n_____ce

14. f_____rce

15. conc_____t

15
14
13
12
11
10
9
8
7
6
5
4
3
2
1

Colour in your score

Test 16

Test 17 Conditionals

A **conditional verb** tells you the action **might** happen (or might have happened), because it **depends** on someone or something else.

I **would** buy an ice-cream if I had any money.

Say if the conditional verbs in bold indicate the past or future tense.

1. If it stops raining we **might go** out. _____

2. If I had searched I **would have found** my watch. _____

3. She **would have passed** her test if she had tried harder. _____

4. I **might go** to America next year. _____

5. If I had heard the alarm I **would have got** up. _____

6. I **could have saved** my money but I didn't. _____

7. I **might play** cricket tomorrow. _____

8. If I were in charge I **would give** everyone a holiday. _____

9. If you won the Lottery what **would** you **buy**? _____

10. I **could have won** the race if I hadn't fallen over. _____

11. I **should have left** while I had the chance. _____

12. No one **would notice** if you went later. _____

13. How much **would** it **cost** to buy that dress? _____

14. I **would have read** the book if you hadn't disturbed me. _____

15. If you come to town with me I **might buy** you a present. _____

Colour in your score

Test 17

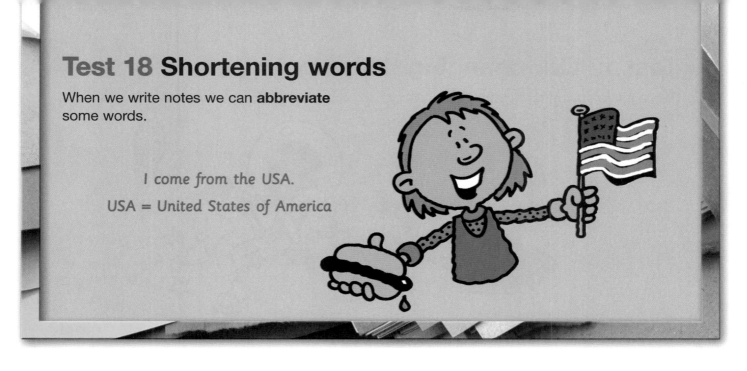

Test 18 Shortening words

When we write notes we can **abbreviate** some words.

I come from the USA.

USA = United States of America

Match up each abbreviation with its meaning.

1.	kph	United Nations
2.	dept	note well
3.	PTO	Crescent
4.	UN	kilometres per hour
5.	Rd	Her (or His) Royal Highness
6.	anon	please reply
7.	etc	Member of Parliament
8.	NB	department
9.	RSVP	Road
10.	BC	please turn over
11.	Sq	Before Christ
12.	Cresc	United Kingdom
13.	MP	anonymous
14.	UK	Square
15.	HRH	etcetera

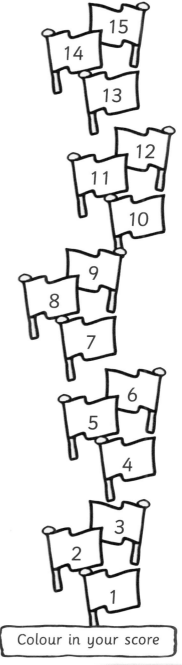

Colour in your score

Test 18

Test 19 Our changing language

Our language is **changing** all the time. Words **fall out of use** and **new words** enter our language.

A **cobbler** made shoes.
We no longer use this word much.

An **astronaut** flies in space.
This is a new space-age word.

Match up these old words with their meanings.

1.	frock	hat
2.	quaff	drinking cup
3.	bonnet	dress
4.	satchel	container for coal
5.	guinea	drink
6.	tinker	an old coin
7.	goblet	schoolbag
8.	scuttle	a man who mended pots

Complete these new 'computer' words.

9. mon____ ____or

10. m____ ____em

11. key____ ____ ____rd

12. e-m____ ____ ____

13. ____ous____

14. inter____ ____ ____

15. w____bs____ ____ ____

Colour in your score

Test 19

Test 20 Formal language

We speak to each other **informally**.   **Official language** is more **formal**.

Match up the formal words or phrases with their informal meanings.

1. forename

2. marital status

3. block letters

4. nationality

5. occupation

6. I beg your pardon.

7. Entrance forbidden!

8. duplicate

9. beverages

10. consume

11. on the reverse

12. remuneration

13. dwelling

14. Smoking prohibited!

15. append

capital letters

the work you do

drinks

on the back

first name

No smoking

whether you are married or single

pay

what country you come from

sorry

eat

attach

You are not allowed in.

where you live

a copy

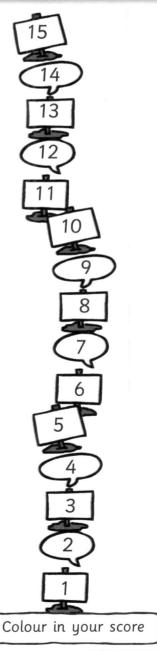

Colour in your score

Test 21 Changing words

We can often change a **root word** by adding a **prefix**.

We can often change a **root word** by adding a **suffix**.

discomfort ⟵ comfort ⟶ comfortable
(root word + prefix) (root word) (root word + suffix)

Choose the correct prefix to complete each word.

1. _____board (a/be)

2. _____loved (a/be)

3. _____mature (in/im)

4. _____considerate (in/im)

5. _____legible (ir/il)

6. _____responsible (ir/il)

7. _____noculars (bi/tri)

8. _____dent (bi/tri)

Work out the root word of each of these words.

9. accidentally _____

10. clumsily _____

11. suspicious _____

12. angry _____

13. circular _____

14. metallic _____

15. sensible _____

Colour in your score

Test 21

Test 22 More about complex sentences

A **complex sentence** contains a **main clause** and a **subordinate** (less important) **clause**. The subordinate clause may not make sense on its own.

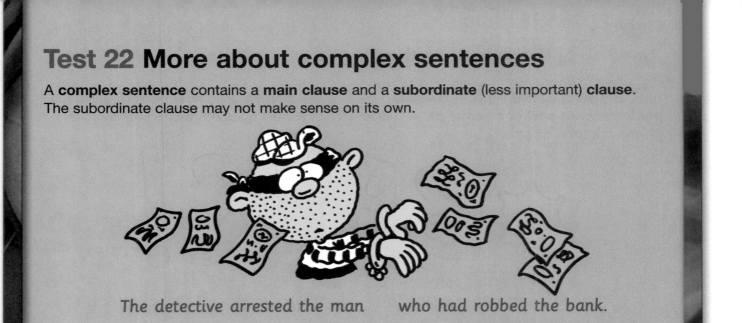

The detective arrested the man   who had robbed the bank.

main clause   subordinate clause

Join up each main clause with a sensible subordinate clause.

1. The children started talking   although I watered them.

2. Tom's mum was cross   because the gate was open.

3. The flowers did not grow   where I saw huge skyscrapers.

4. I visited New York   when the teacher went out.

5. The dog escaped   which I had lost.

6. It often rains   when she saw his messy bedroom.

7. I found the key   so I always carry an umbrella.

Now try these.

8. I had a bath   before she left.

9. The audience cheered   because it was starving.

10. My aunt hugged me   who is very naughty.

11. The lady asked the way   because I was so muddy.

12. Abdi is the boy   when she got lost.

13. Mrs Cane won the Lottery   before it got dark.

14. The child ran home   when the band played.

15. The dog ate hungrily   so she bought a new house.

Colour in your score

Test 22

Test 23 Phrases and clauses

A **clause** may be used either as a **whole sentence** or as **part of a sentence**. A clause always contains a verb.

A **phrase** does **not** contain a **verb**. A phrase does **not make sense** on its own.

The balloon popped
clause

with a loud bang.
phrase

Write whether each of these is a clause or a phrase.

1. Sarah slipped over. _____

2. in a muddy puddle _____

3. after the programme _____

4. Sam rode her bike. _____

5. The spacecraft landed on the hill. _____

6. as fast as a flash _____

7. The lady put down her bag. _____

8. until next time _____

9. The lion pounced on the gazelle. _____

10. near the lake _____

11. until midnight _____

12. The baby smiled at me. _____

13. Some cars have big boots. _____

14. all green and slimy _____

15. A giraffe has a long neck. _____

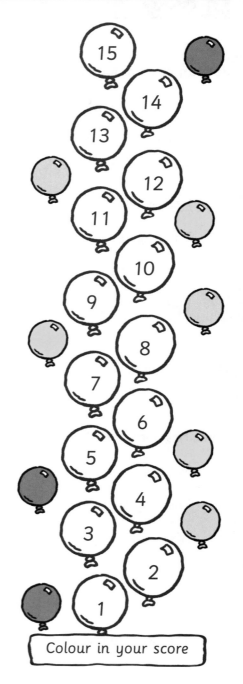

Colour in your score

Test 23

Test 24 **More punctuation**

It is important to check that your **punctuation** is correct.

Fill in the missing punctuation marks.

1. The monkeys were playing in the tree____

2. Amir bought eggs____ milk, bread and flour at the shop.

3. "Where do you live____" she asked.

4. "Get out____" he shouted.

5. The dog____s tail was wagging.

6. ____What book are you reading?" Shiraz asked.

7. After tea____ Mark watched TV.

8. Mrs Best said____ "Where is my bag?"

9. It isn____t a nice day.

10. The toy didn____t cost much.

11. "Come with me____ Ben," the teacher said.

12. "Stop that at once____" Mr Khan demanded.

13. The dog, a small poodle____ yapped loudly.

14. The door was open____ inviting him to enter.

15. "When I____ve got enough money, I'll retire," Mr Farr said.

Colour in your score

Test 25 Another spelling rule

When a word has one vowel before a single final consonant, we double the consonant before adding a **suffix** – if the last syllable is stressed.

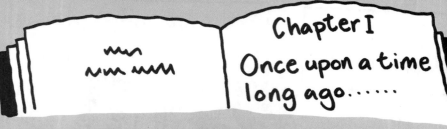

Chapter I
Once upon a time
long ago......

begin – beginning

Add the suffix ing. Write the word you make.

1. rebel _____

2. admit _____

3. forget _____

4. prefer _____

5. signal _____

Add the suffix ed. Write the word you make.

6. regret _____

7. transmit _____

8. travel _____

9. occur _____

10. control _____

Take the suffix off. Write the root word you are left with.

11. fulfilled _____

12. forbidding _____

13. referred _____

14. marvelled _____

15. omitting _____

Colour in your score

Test 26 Long and short vowels

win

wine

Short vowels make the
sound of the letter.

Long vowels say the
name of the letter.

Use the signs to show whether the vowels are long ‾ or short �’.

1.   sigh

2.   plush

3.   truth

4.   wild

5.   swam

6.   desk

7.   show

8.   shy

9.   flip

10.   drip

11.   text

12.   stay

13.   most

14.   blind

15.   lost

Colour in your score

Test 26

Test 27 Common word endings

It is helpful to learn the spelling of **common word endings**.

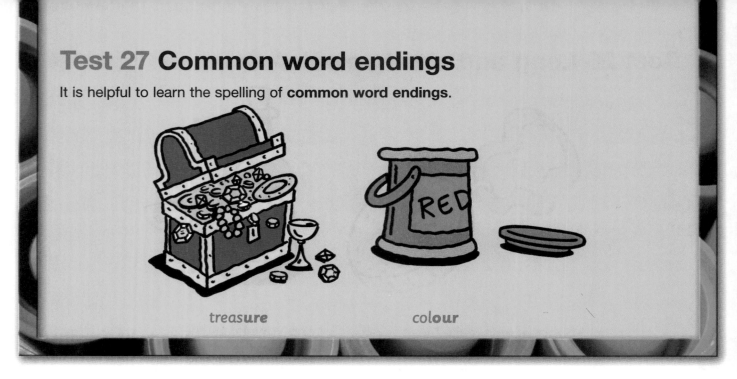

treasure   colour

Choose our or ure to complete each word.

1. flav_____   9. lab_____

2. cult_____   10. col_____

3. furnit_____   11. fig_____

4. fav_____   12. fail_____

5. mixt_____   13. vig_____

6. hon_____   14. harb_____

7. vap_____   15. capt_____

8. inj_____

Colour in your score

Test 28 More common word endings

It is helpful to learn the spelling of **common word endings**.

nurs**ery**   laborat**ory**   di**ary**

Each of these words is spelt incorrectly. Spell each word correctly.

1. machinary _____

2. factery _____

3. delivory _____

4. dictionery _____

5. observatery _____

6. discovary _____

7. granery _____

8. laboratary _____

9. jewellory _____

10. dormitery _____

11. flattary _____

12. estuory _____

13. militery _____

14. territery _____

15. librory _____

Colour in your score

Test 28

Test 29 Similes

A **simile** is when one thing is compared to another. We often use the word **as** in similes.

Shh!

The children were **as** quiet **as** mice.

Complete these well-known similes with these words.

tortoise	swan	bat	fox	ox	mule	lion	elephant

1. as blind as a _____

2. as obstinate as a _____

3. as crafty as a _____

4. as heavy as an _____

5. as fierce as a _____

6. as strong as an _____

7. as graceful as a _____

8. as slow as a _____

Now do these.

thin	regular	fit	easy	safe	flat	sour

9. as _____ as a fiddle

10. as _____ as vinegar

11. as _____ as a pancake

12. as _____ as a rake

13. as _____ as clockwork

14. as _____ as ABC

15. as _____ as a bank

15
14
13
12
11
10
9
8
7
6
5
4
3
2
1

Colour in your score

Test 29

Test 30 Word games

We can learn a lot by playing **word games**. They can help us with our **spelling** and help to **improve our vocabulary**.

Use a dictionary to help you work out these clues.

These words all begin with she.

1. a law officer _____

2. a place for protection _____

3. very steep _____

4. large scissors _____

These words all begin with go.

5. a hairy berry _____

6. a prickly shrub _____

7. glasses for protection _____

8. a young goose _____

These words all begin with pea.

9. quiet _____

10. a bird with beautiful feathers _____

11. a kind of fuel _____

12. grows in a pod underground _____

These words all begin with ant.

13. old and valuable _____

14. an animal like a deer _____

15. kind of aerial _____

Colour in your score

Test 30

ANSWERS

Test 1
The missing vowels are in **bold**.
1. di**a**mond
2. acc**i**dental
3. entr**a**nce
4. diff**e**rent
5. deod**o**rant
6. m**y**stery
7. cru**e**l
8. inter**e**sting
9. eff**o**rt
10. mon**a**stery
11. lunch**e**on
12. sep**a**rate
13. butt**o**n
14. skel**e**ton
15. phot**o**grapher

Test 2
1. friend
2. assist
3. metre
4. able
5. beg
6. engine
7. change
8. king
9. bright
10. perfect
11. fix
12. serve
13. man
14. duck
15. hold

Test 3
1. I had my favourite meal – spaghetti.
2. I love apples – Ben hates them!
3. One boy looked strange – he was wearing a mask.
4. I won a prize – for coming first in spelling.
5. My uncle appeared – laughing as usual.
6. Christopher Wren built a famous cathedral – St Paul's.
7. Mr Smith has a sports car – a silver one.
8. I love music – especially pop music.
9. On the sand I found something interesting – an old chest.
10. Work hard – or you will never get a good job!
11. I know someone very brave – my friend Sarah.
12. Tom collects insects – especially beetles.
13. Mount Pico is in the Azores – a group of islands.
14. I saw a good programme last night – a monster film.
15. My room overlooks a wood – a small dark wood.

Test 4
1. <u>door</u>
2. <u>man</u>
3. <u>wind</u>
4. <u>children</u>
5. <u>car</u>
6. <u>ride</u>
7. <u>ate</u>
8. <u>will try</u>
9. <u>cooked</u>
10. <u>cross</u>
11. <u>slippery</u>
12. <u>rough</u>
13. <u>colourful</u>
14. <u>scary</u>
15. <u>favourite</u>

Test 5
1. nevertheless
2. or
3. because
4. as
5. before
6. when
7. so that
8. if
9. then
10. in case
11. until
12. however
13. but
14. as soon as
15. because

Test 6
Answers 1–8: the correct prefix is in **bold**.
1. **auto**graph
2. **il**legal
3. **de**port
4. **im**patient
5. **dis**approve
6. **mis**behave
7. **em**bark
8. **pre**arrange
9. confidence
10. bakery
11. communication
12. student
13. replacement
14. service
15. friendliness

Test 7
1. active
2. passive
3. active
4. passive
5. passive
6. active
7. active
8. passive
9. active
10. passive
11. active
12. active
13. passive
14. passive
15. active

Test 8
1. ballerina
2. piano
3. spaghetti
4. opera
5. confetti
6. buffet
7. cabaret
8. bracket
9. bouquet
10. duvet
11. skipper
12. sketch
13. schooner
14. smuggle
15. landscape

Test 9
1. knowledge
2. believe
3. mathematics
4. piece
5. ambitious
6. chocolate
7. business
8. government
9. separate
10. breadth
11. conscience
12. whole
13. island
14. cereal
15. soldier

Test 10
The missing punctuation marks are in **bold**.
1. Dr Turner's car was green.
2. Mrs Brown, who was getting angry, shouted loudly.
3. "Don't cross the busy road," Mrs Smith warned Tom.
4. Do you like oranges or lemons best?
5. During the night, it rained heavily.
6. "Where's my dinner?" the giant roared.
7. "I hate sprouts!" Sam shouted.
8. My brother hates music – but I love it.
9. In my pocket I had a coin, a sweet, a tissue and a badge.
10. The teachers' room is next to the office.
11. Where are you going?
12. I'm nearly eleven.
13. The film doesn't begin for an hour.
14. "Hands up!" the robber shouted.
15. "My job can be dangerous," the police officer said.

Test 11
1. signal
2. signature
3. design
4. liberty
5. liberal
6. liberate
7. audience
8. audible
9. auditorium
10. script
11. describe
12. scribble
13. spectator
14. spectacles
15. spectacular

Test 12
1. 1
2. 1
3. 2
4. 2
5. 1
6. 1
7. 2
8. 2
9. 2
10. 1
11. 2
12. 2
13. 2
14. 2
15. 1

Test 13
1. grow fonder
2. choosers
3. than words
4. flock together
5. twice shy
6. a silver lining
7. spoil the broth
8. in one basket
9. less speed
10. the sun shines
11. than one
12. never
13. you leap
14. out of mind
15. saves nine

Test 14
The missing second syllable is in **bold**.
1. de**ter**mine
2. u**ni**form
3. hos**pi**tal
4. ex**cel**lent
5. at**ten**tion
6. dif**fer**ent
7. ad**ven**ture
8. syl**la**ble
9. pa**ra**chute
10. in**tro**duce
11. be**gin**ning
12. e**lec**tric
13. Sep**tem**ber
14. pun**ish**ment
15. fa**vour**ite

Test 15
1. occasion
2. privilege
3. fascinate
4. excitement
5. immediate
6. recognise
7. mathematics
8. disappear
9. control
10. marriage
11. rhubarb
12. temporary
13. disastrous
14. scissors
15. environment